POEMS

POEMS

POEMS

By RACHEL FIELD

Decorations by the author

THE MACMILLAN COMPANY
New York

Library of Congress catalog card number: 57-9894

ACKNOWLEDGMENTS

Many of the poems included in this book first appeared in the *New York Herald Tribune* in F.P.A.'s column The Conning Tower and The Three Owls column edited by Anne Carroll Moore. A number of the poems have been used in children's magazines—*Child Life, St. Nicholas, American Girl, John Martin's Book,* and *The Horn Book.*

Acknowledgment is made to the following publishers for their permission to reproduce copyrighted material:

Doubleday & Company: "If Once You Have Slept on an Island," "The Animal Store," "I'd Like To Be a Lighthouse," and "Tides," from *Taxis and Toadstools* by Rachel Field, copyright 1926 by Doubleday & Company.

Good Housekeeping Magazine: "Our House," reprinted by permission of Good Housekeeping.

The New Yorker Magazine: "Early Morning" (1934) and "The Uncharted" (1942) copyrighted in the respective years shown by The New Yorker Magazine, Inc.

With the exception of the following poems published here for the first time—"For Us in War-Time," "For Father's Day," "Japanese Gardeners," "My Neighbor's Fig Tree," "Testament," "Pygmy Song"—the rest of the poems were once included in the authors books, *Pointed People, Branches Green, Christmas Time, Eliza and the Elves* and *Fear Is the Thorn,* published by The Macmillan Company.

CONTENTS

On Christmas

Fairy Folk

Branches
Green

A Charm for Spring Flowers

Who sees the first marsh marigold
Shall count more wealth than hands can hold.

Who bends a knee where violets grow
A hundred secret things shall know.

Who finds hepatica's dim blue
Shall have his dearest wish come true.

Who spies on lady-slippers fair
Shall keep a heart as light as air.

But whosoever toucheth not
One petal, sets no root in pot,

He shall be blessed of earth and sky
Till under them he, too, shall lie.

The Hills

Sometimes I think the hills
That loom across the harbor
Lie there like sleeping dragons,
Crouched one above another,
With trees for tufts of fur
Growing all up and down
The ridges and humps of their backs,
And orange cliffs for claws
Dipped in the sea below.
Sometimes a wisp of smoke
Rises out of the hollows,
As if in their dragon sleep
They dreamed of strange old battles.

What if the hills should stir
Some day and stretch themselves,
Shake off the clinging trees
And all the clustered houses?

If I Were a Tree

If I were a little tree like you,
　Instead of a child like me,
I would dig my roots in the good black earth
　And toss my arms to the sea.
I would be twisted and small like you
　For the winds to bend me low,
And drops of rain on my twigs would lie
　Like silver beads in a row.
I would be like you as ever I could—
　Green-spiked and needle-y,
If I were a little tree like you,
　Instead of a child like me!

In Spring

By every doorway lilacs lean,
Tufts of bloom in a mist of green.
The river goes blue and curving by
Under a bluer arch of sky.
There's a white cloud over the cherry tree
Like a little lost sail in a distant sea.
But never a thing that I can do
To show that the Spring is in me too!

My Neighbor's Fig Tree

In disregard of anchored root
My neighbor's fig tree, thick with fruit,
An invitation mute extends
Across the fence. Each branch that bends
Its load, sun-warmed and dark of skin,
Like swelling purses rich within,
Defies the laws of property
To make a sinner out of me!
My neighbor's fig tree, innocent
Of boundary, has no intent
To foster crimes of appetite,
Ulterior motives, wrong or right
Concern it less than sun and air
And that first law—the urge to bear.

A Vow in Mid-summer

Now let us sing how purple vetch
    Keeps daisies company,
With devil's paint-brush, copper tipped,
    In fields above the sea.

And let us mark how grasses bow
    Before the wind's swift greeting,
And how the shadows on the hills
    Are dark and lean and fleeting.

But let us never quite forget
    When orange lilies glow,
To bless the hands that set them out
    In dooryards, years ago.

Pasture Song

Oh, for the beat of changing tides;
 For sheep bells faintly clear;
For brooks that tinkle from stone to stone,
A thrush that calls in woods alone,
 Morning, evening, afternoon.
 Oh, for a sheep bell clear!

Oh, for sweet slopes of pasture grass;
 For a path that winds and winds;
For juniper and twisted trees
Against the shine of windy seas,
 Morning, evening, afternoon.
 Oh, for a path that winds!

After Rain

See how upon bare twigs they lie,
Raindrops, lately of the sky—
Balls of crystal, rounder far
Than any earthen berries are.
Phantom fruits begot of air
Fashioned for no human fare.

Fir Trees

Little green, green fir trees,
Trooping down the headlands
Where the old sea tugs and seethes
At the farthest ledges—
Little bristling fir trees,
No one trims your branches;
Woodsmen with their axes sharp
Always pass you by.
Never shall you tower
Like your inland neighbors;
You the wind and sea have kept
Small as gypsy children,
Shaggy-haired and shy,
Crowding close together
Wrapt in cloaks of tattered green
Your sharp brown arms poke through—
Little sea-dwarfed fir trees,
Luckier than your fellows,
Young as waves and fairies are,
And every wise small star.

Rebellion in September

Five and twelve make? Oh, dear me,
How the red leaves shine on the maple tree.

Wild geese fly in a long dark line!
Seven times seven are forty-nine.

Crickets chirp where the grass grows brown—
Which is the verb and which the noun?

Asters grow white and gentians blue—
What are the boundaries of Peru?

How can I name the Presidents,
When corn stalks rise like golden tents?

Eleven times three are thirty-three—
Why wasn't I born a bird or a tree?

Gentians May Not Stay

Gentians may not stay
In accustomed places.
A season, maybe two,
And they must steal away,
Folding up their blue
Fringes secretly
As bands of gypsies do,
Peddling charms and laces
At the edge of frost.
But when they have gone
Woodsmoke lingers there,
Dim and ghostly blue
On the autumn air.
Gentians may not stay,
They are gypsies too,
Fugitive as lost tunes,
Brief as morning dew.

Spring Signs

Now is the time that hills put on
A smoky blue, untinged with green,
When sorrel-red and cinnamon
In brief possession hold the scene;
When robins, orange breasted, shiver,
And wrens and burnished grackles scold;
When every brook is a rushing river,
And crocus companies brave the cold;
When freshly painted cars speed by,
And dogs and children skip and caper;—
Now is the time when such as I
Must set down rhymes on sheets of paper!

A Summer Morning

I saw dawn creep across the sky,
And all the gulls go flying by.
I saw the sea put on its dress
Of blue mid-summer loveliness,
And heard the trees begin to stir
Green arms of pine and juniper.
I heard the wind call out and say:
"Get up, my dear, it is to-day!"

Back Country

Wherever there were gaps between
Each steep-set farm, the woods were green
And brown, with shafts of sun that made
Emerald fire in bristling shade.
Dooryard roses hummed with bees.
Cows stood staring, up to their knees
In an old mill pond where no wheels churn.
Sheep, in laurel and clumps of fern,
Grayer than bowlders, moved one way.
Every cart with its load of hay
Had creaking wheels of faded blue
Like the flapping overalls askew
On the canted scarecrow, lone and lorn,
Solemnly guarding his field of corn.
The crossroads sign had tumbled down
So I asked a boy and girl with brown
Bare feet the way when they went by
Quick as rabbits, and twice as shy.

Heard at Night

The tree-toad's a town crier
   With faint and rusty bell
That through long summer evenings
   Rings out a far "All's well."

And from the swampy thicket
   The frogs croak, like a score
Of old men gathered nightly
   About some village store.

But shrill as ancient fiddle
   Beneath a blindman's bow
Crickets and grasshoppers must play
   The only tune they know.

The Little Rose Tree

Every rose on the little tree
Is making a different face at me!

Some look surprised when I pass by,
And others droop—but they are shy.

These two whose heads together press
Tell secrets I could never guess.

Some have their heads thrown back to sing,
And all the buds are listening.

I wonder if the gardener knows,
Or if he calls each just a rose?

Wild Cranberry

Were these the fairy apples Snow-White knew,
   Scarlet sided and white?
And shall these lips of mine taste magic too,
   And spells, at the first sharp bite?
I never stooped to pick them where they grew,
   Incredible and bright,
But the old tale has taken me anew
And I have half believed it might be true.

Wild Honey

The wild bees cluster and crowd and hum
In the dooryard's blue delphinium.
They tilt in clover and jostling, fetch
Sweet on sweet from the purple vetch,
With never a pause in their anxious haste,
Making honey no lips shall taste.

What of your golden comb, wild bees,
Stored secure in some ancient tree's
Hidden hollow? What of this sweet
None shall discover? That none shall eat?
What of the treasure none shall find
In the secret places of the mind?

A Rhyme for Trees

The birch tree's trunk is beautiful,
Whiter than shining breast of gull
Laid to the steep blue slopes of air.
Maples are gay as a county fair
In red and yellow for early frost.
A pine has rugged greenness tossed
On windy branches. A balsam fir
Is thick with needles, spicier
Than scents of ancient Araby.
The elm makes dappled tracery
Of shade on lawn and village street.
The spruce's bark is sticky-sweet.
Horse-chestnut flowers like steeples rise.
A poplar is full of leafy sighs.
In fall the oak spreads a russet dome.
The apple is gnarled as a friendly gnome,
Crooked of bough, twisted of root.
But a mountain ash has fiery fruit,
And who in his pocket hides a spray,
Magic will keep by night and day.

Japanese Gardeners

Along the steep pitched headlands
  Above the heaving blue,
Each day the same small figures keep
  Their rendez-vous with dew,
With sun and sea mist, earth and air,
  As patiently they burrow
More wrinkled than the seeds they plant,
  Brown as the soil they furrow.
More tireless than the delving mole,
  Yet warier than the crow,
Sturdy as spiders, squat and sure,
  They summon row on row.
Their epitaph the living green
  Of earth's fertility
In patterns geometrical
  Between the hills and sea.

Thoughts
and Feelings

Prayer for a Child

Bless this milk and bless this bread.
Bless this soft and waiting bed
Where I presently shall be
Wrapped in sweet security.
Through the darkness, through the night
Let no danger come to fright
My sleep till morning once again
Beckons at the window pane.
Bless the toys whose shapes I know,
The shoes that take me to and fro
Up and down and everywhere.
Bless my little painted chair.
Bless the lamplight, bless the fire,
Bless the hands that never tire
In their loving care of me.
Bless my friends and family.
Bless my Father and my Mother
And keep us close to one another.
Bless other children, far and near,
And keep them safe and free from fear.
So let me sleep and let me wake
In peace and health, for Jesus' sake.

AMEN

For Father's Day

Here a little child I wait
Father dear, beside our gate.
When the sun is dropping low
And tired birds to branches go
That's the time I would not roam
Lest I miss your coming home.
And if God should chance to be
Looking from the sky at me
He would smile there in the blue
For He is Our Father, too.

The Uncharted

The boundaries of heaven may be
Less wide than night's immensity;
Less high than snowy peak or spire.
A lamplit pane, a kindled fire,
A room, an acre, or a mile,
Or the brief space it takes a smile
To cross the threshold of a heart—
These no cartographer may chart,
Or instrument have power to give
The latitudes by which we live.

Song for a Blue Roadster

Fly, Roadster, fly!
  The sun is high,
Gold are the fields
  We hurry by,
Green are the woods
  As we slide through,
Past harbor and headland,
  Blue on blue.

Fly, Roadster, fly!
  The hay smells sweet,
And the flowers fringing
  Each village street,
Where carts are blue,
  And barns are red,
And the road unwinds
  Like a twist of thread.

Fly, Roadster, fly!
  Leave Time behind;
Out of sight
  Shall be out of mind.
Shine and shadow,
  Blue sea, green bough,
Nothing is real
  But Here and Now.

Where?

When winter nights are cold and black,
And the wind walks by
Like the battered and wild old tramp he is,
With a whistle and a sigh—
When the house is full of firelight
And shadows lean and fleet
That chase each other round and round
Till they all meet—
When father reads his paper,
And the others sew,
I sometimes feel inside myself
A little sad and low,
For then I hear their cracked, gay tunes,
And wonder where and how
All the hurdy-gurdy men
Are playing now.

Doorbells

You never know with a doorbell
  Who may be ringing it—
It may be Great-Aunt Cynthia
  To spend the day and knit;
It may be a peddler with things to sell
  (I'll buy some when I'm older),
Or the grocer's boy with his apron on
  And a basket on his shoulder;
It may be the old umbrella-man
  Giving his queer, cracked call,
Or a lady dressed in rustly silk,
  With card-case and parasol.
Doorbells are like a magic game,
  Or the grab-bag at a fair—
You never know when you hear one ring
  Who may be waiting there!

First Thanksgiving

Dear child, be grateful for the sun,
Its day long journey well begun—
Be grateful that it finds you far
From lands where feuds and hatreds are,
Where death wings close, and fear endures
To mask such baby smiles as yours
In shapes grotesque. Be glad and gay
Upon this ancient holiday
For all such benefits as these—
For fertile earth, and fruitful trees.
Be one with every hidden seed
That stirs to every flower or weed.
Be grateful that you too shall know
The selfsame urge that makes them grow
In sun and rain, but never be
Grateful in any wise to me,
Who asks this only—to renew
Acquaintance with the world through you.

Song

Love is a startled bird that sings
   Through a slanting fall of rain.
Love is a bell in the heart that rings
   And echoes through the brain
Long after chiming. Love is a wind
   Spicy and keen and cool.
Love is a silver fish, bright finned,
   That swims in a secret pool.
Love is the apple too far to reach
   High on the orchard tree.
Love is a shell on a lonely beach
   Washed by the tide to me.

A Fire

Why does a fire eat big sticks of wood?
I shouldn't like to have that for my food.
But the flames all lick their lips—it must taste good!

Snow in the City

Snow is out of fashion,
  But it still comes down,
To whiten all the buildings
  In our town;
To dull the noise of traffic;
  To dim each glaring light
With star-shaped feathers
  Of frosty white.
And not the tallest building
  Halfway up the sky;
Or all the trains and busses,
  And taxis scudding by;
And not a million people,
  Not one of them at all,
Can do a thing about the snow
  But let it fall!

The Piper

I had a willow whistle,
　　I piped it on the hill.
The grass reached up, the sky bent down,
　　And all the world grew still.

Now up, now down the rounded holes,
　　My fingers fluttered light,
And little notes came trooping out
　　As thick as elves by night.

They turned themselves into a tune
　　More clear than drops of dew,
More sweet than almond trees, more soft
　　Than clouds the moon slips through.

Oh, good it was to be alone—
　　To pipe there on the hill,
With bending sky, and reaching grass,
　　And all the world grown still.

Burning Leaves

Whenever leaves are burning
And the blue and bitter smoke
Steals up from gardens and roadsides
On evenings in October,
Something in me stirs
And wants to go away.

I may be setting the table,
Or baking a little cake
With edges brown and scalloped.
I may be under the covers
Of the tall four-poster bed
When that scent lays hold on me.

And I would be leaving the fireside,
The willow plates on the dresser,
The quilt with its crazy patches,
For almost any road,
Rain-black or brown and rutty.
For almost any village,
So long as it's not home.

The House in the Woods

Deep in the old pine woods
Where moss like a rug is spread,
Stands a house with crumbling walls
And a roof of rusty red.

Grass sprouts in every chink;
The eaves are filmed with green.
If I crossed the threshold worn,
I should nevermore be seen.

For who but a witch would live
Where woods press tree on tree?
So I scurry by that place
Lest a spell be laid on me.

In Praise of Dust

Dust is such a pleasant thing—
A soft gray kind of covering
For furniture, whereon to draw
Letters and pictures by the score.
Why won't the grown-ups let dust stay,
Instead of brushing it away?

Dancing

I cannot dance in a stuffy room
   To the music of a ball;
Indoors where lights and people are
   I cannot dance at all.

But out on the lawn of an afternoon
   Jane takes my hand, and we
Dance gayer than all the poplar leaves,
   Or ships on a windy sea.

Early Morning Song

Nothing fairer than the light
On petals opening, gold and white,
To the morning, to the blue,
In a world of song and dew.

Nothing fairer than two eyes
That behold with shy surprise
The miracle no man can stay—
Darkness turning into day.

Northern Song

Morning comes over the eastern islands;
Twilight waits in the western hills.
High in the north above my roof-top
Night's starry dipper hangs and spills
Dark and inexhaustible waters,
Oblivion's dew for the restless brain;
Balm for the wakeful; peace for the sleeper,
Sweeter than music, softer than rain.

Blue

There at the old wood's edge
I saw a bluebird fly.
And its wings beat bright against
The paler blue of sky;
They seemed to burn a way
Into the sky and me,
Till my heart stood still in a hush
Of ecstasy.
I watched that bluebird fly,
And knew with a queer dull pain
That nothing now can ever seem
So blue to me again!

The Quiet Child

By day it's a very good girl am I;
I sit by the fire and sew,
I darn the stockings and sweep the floors
And hang the pots in a row.
But, oh, by night when the candle's out
And my bedroom black as pitch,
I've just to crackle my thumbs to turn
Into a wild bad witch.

Nights of storm and nights of stars
Are all the same to me—
It's up on my broom and straddle the wind
As it whips my pigtails free.
Over the chimney pots to go,
Past the jumbled lights of towns,
With the hosts of good black trees beyond,
And dim sheep-sprinkled downs.

No one knows when morning comes
And I'm back in bed once more,
With tangled hair and eyes a-blink
From the sunshine on the floor—
No one knows of that witch who rode
In the windy dark and wild—
And I let them praise my sober ways,
And call me a quiet child!

I Want a Pasture

I want a pasture for next door neighbor;
   The sea to be just across the way.
I want to stand at my door for hours
   Talking and passing the time of day
Unhurried, as country people do
Season on season, a whole year through.

I want to give greeting to frost and sun;
   To gossip with thunder and tides and bees;
To mark the doings of wind in boughs;
   Watch apples redden on crookéd trees.
I want to hail each passing thing
That moves, fleet-footed, by fin, or wing.

I want far islands to grow familiar
   As neighbors' faces; clouds be more plain
Than granite bowlder; than web of spider
   Patterned with intricate drops of rain.
I want to be wise as the oldest star,
Young as the waves and grasses are.

For Us in War-time

While birds sing on, no less aware
Of black winged death and hidden snare,

And through earth scarred by fire and gun
Brown seeds still push to find the sun;

While roses bloom and apples dare
To ripen in bomb-shattered air,

So long as butterfly and bee
Perform their ordered destiny,

And crickets chirp against the roar
Of man-made thunderings of war,—

Should we be less than these who brave
With bloom and song the open grave?

Should we betray love's ancient trust
And bow our hearts to meet the dust?

A Northwest Window

This window opens wide to sky and sea;
   To sand and sunsets and a twisted tree;
And any eye that will may take delight
   In windy blue by day, or moon by night;
In blown dune grass, and lighthouse, white and far,
   That shines at evening like a nearer star.
This window opens wide to sea and sky,
   And who need farther look? Not you, not I.

Skyscrapers

Do skyscrapers ever grow tired
   Of holding themselves up high?
Do they ever shiver on frosty nights
   With their tops against the sky?
Do they feel lonely sometimes,
   Because they have grown so tall?
Do they ever wish they could lie right down
   And never get up at all?

Our House

Our house is small as houses go,
The walls are white and the roof is low.
No one passing by would say:—
"I'll build a house like that someday!"
But there's a chimney for smoke to climb
From the fireplace in winter time.
There's a slit for letters in the door,
A yard behind and a lawn before
With dandelion buttons dressed,
And a linden tree where starlings nest.
The windows stare like watching eyes.
There's a wicket gate the proper size
For swinging on and looking through,
And a bench that once was painted blue.
Our house is like no house I know
On any street, in any row,—
For brick or shingle, tall or wide,
A house is yours when you're inside!

Ticking Clocks

The cuckoo clock on the nursery wall
Has a voice that is woody and brown and small,
And all day long in happy rhyme
Its ticks are saying, *Plenty of Time,*
  There's always plenty of Time.

On the mantel over the fireplace
The marble clock with the gilded face
And chimes as sweet as a sea-drowned bell
Says over and over, *Time will tell,*
  Yes, Time will always tell.

The old hall clock with the pendulum
Beats every hour like a drum.
Heavy and deep, from far inside,
Hear how it booms out, *Time and Tide,*
  Solemnly, Time and Tide.

My Inside-Self

My Inside-Self and my Outside-Self
  Are different as can be.
My Outside-Self wears gingham smocks,
  And very round is she,
With freckles sprinkled on her nose,
  And smoothly parted hair,
And clumsy feet that cannot dance
  In heavy shoes and square.

But, oh my little Inside-Self—
  In gown of misty rose
She dances lighter than a leaf
  On blithe and twinkling toes;
Her hair is blowing gold, and if
  You chanced her face to see,
You would not think she could belong
  To staid and sober me!

Testament

Hate is abroad, I know, my dear,
Walking the world with its comrade Fear,
Sowing dark seeds of dread and doubt
While statesmen argue and newsboys shout.
Their words like evil echoes ring
To drown such songs as I can sing.
Yet though my rhymes sound shrill and thin
As crickets' chirp against the din
Of thunder, still must I give praise
For fire-lit nights and sun-warmed days;
For bird calls, watery and sweet
That welcome morning to our street;
For flowers, punctual as the clock,—
Jonquil and daisy, rose and stock;
For smell of coffee, stir of rain,
For round eyes at the window pane;
For laughter brimming unafraid
In this small world our love has made.
And if my song be choked in dust
It will not matter—sing I must.

Thoughts

Thoughts are so queer, you never know
What they will be about.
You fish for them inside your mind,
And when you pull one out—
You may have caught a devil-fish,
Or a little shiny trout!

Rain in the City

All the streets are a-shine with rain
The other side of my window pane.
Each motor car unrolls a track
Of red or green on the asphalt's black.
Beneath umbrellas people ply
Like giant toadstools stalking by.

Rainy Day Rhyme

When stones across the way are sleek
   With wet, when windows blur,
Then in my heart small songs must start
   Their swift and secret stir.
They prick a way through this poor clay,
   And if I let them climb,—
Why, who can tell but one might swell
   And flower into rhyme?

Whistles

I never even hear
The boats that pass by day;
By night they seem so near,
A-whistling down the bay,
That I can almost understand
The things their whistles say.

I've waked sometimes all warm
In my bed, when eerily
I have heard them out of the dark
A-whistling cheerily
To tell the sleepy folk on land
All's well at sea.

Rainy Nights

Always on rainy nights
When my candle is blown out
And I am all alone,
I hear strange footsteps fall
Out in the dark and wet—
Footsteps that only come
With the rain, and go with it—
Noisily swashing by
Like the boots of buccaneers,
Or the tread of old sea captains
Tramping on salty decks
Of ships with figureheads,
So old the sea has forgotten
Their names and the ports they sailed from.
Sometimes in soft spring rains
The steps are light and hurried,
Pattering by like children
With little scuffling sounds,
Up and down in the dark
Long corridors of night.
Whose footsteps are they, and why
Do they come and go like that,
And what do they want in the rain?

The Restless Balloon

Gay balloon,
Round and blue,
I should like
To fly with you.
Must you sail,
You pretty thing,
Where brave star fleets
Go voyaging?
Oh, don't tug so
At the string!

People

and Places

The Old Scotch Bagpiper

Up the long gray streets,
In the whirling snow,
He pipes to the houses
Row on row.

Round the pipes his lips are pressed,
And he crooks his arm to make a nest
For the worn red bag that fills and plays
The skirling notes of vanished days,
And he sways like those dark and bending trees
That cling to cliffs by northern seas.

The passersby all smile to see
His ulster flapping crazily—
Not one of them is glad to hear
The tune that once gave kings good cheer,
That once bade kilted armies go
With clattering swords against the foe,
Or sounded that Queen Mary should
Put on her crown in Holyrood.

Up the long gray streets,
In the whirling snow,
He pipes to the houses
Row on row.

Manhattan Lullaby

(FOR RICHARD—ONE DAY OLD)

Now lighted windows climb the dark,
  The streets are dim with snow.
Like tireless beetles, amber-eyed,
  The creeping taxis go.
Cars roar through caverns made of steel,
  Shrill sounds the siren horn,
And people dance and die and wed—
  And boys like you are born.

"London Bridge"

"London Bridge is falling down,"
Down, down, down—
Out on the green the old game goes.
Bobbing heads and scuffling toes,
Little bodies, round and free,
Whirling, mingling dizzily,
Hands stretched out all warm and brown
To grasp and reach again;
And always comes the old refrain—
"London Bridge is falling down,"
Down, down, down.

Curly Hair

She must have curly thoughts, I know;
Yet she has never told me so.
But I can guess because her hair
Just crinkles crisply everywhere
About her head, and tries to hide
All the merry thoughts inside.
And though her lips will never tell,
Curls can't keep secrets very well!

Some People

Isn't it strange some people make
    You feel so tired inside,
Your thoughts begin to shrivel up
    Like leaves all brown and dried!

But when you're with some other ones,
    It's stranger still to find
Your thoughts as thick as fireflies
    All shiny in your mind!

The Old Postman

There's an old postman that I know,
Up and down I see him go,
But oh! so lagging move his feet
From house to house along the street.
His back is bent with a double stoop,
And his shoulders have a sagging droop,
Queer just letters could bend him so—
Small, light squares a breath can blow
With one quick puff so far and wide.
I think it must be things inside:
All the thoughts that letters tell:
Who are sick and who are well:
Who are merry, who forlorn:
People buried; babies born.
Letters sweet like songs of birds,
Letters full of wise long words,
Letters big and letters small—
Our old postman brings them all
In the bag upon his back
(Strange, I think, it doesn't crack!)
As up and down the streets he bears
Everybody's joys and cares.

The Scissors-Grinder

Over the road when Spring begins
  And fields drop green to the bay,
Before you have seen him a long way off
  You can hear him call and say:
"Knives to grind; Scissors to mend!
  Bring out your knives to-day!"

Brown is his face as a last year's cone;
  His eyes as blue as the sea;
And his body stoops with a listing cant
  Like a windswept cedar tree.

Are there always children who watch for him
  When winter is at an end—
For his bell and his cry and his slanting self
  To turn some far road's bend?
Does he follow the Spring from place to place
  With his "Knives and Scissors to mend"?

Lament for Organ Grinders

Organ Grinders, have a care,
Didn't you know our city air
Can't be cluttered with anything
Useless as last year's tunes that sing,
Husky and sad, and gay and thin,
Above the torrent of traffic's din?
Didn't you know it's a crime to play
For the scattered coins that fall your way,
To play for nothing, like as not,
Where children swarm by some vacant lot?
If you had pretzels or fruit to sell
You might have lingered. Fare you well.
It's begging to hold your hats for a tip,
And children must learn to walk, not skip.
Better be off without delay,
Trundle your musical carts away.
Riverside Drive to Avenue B.
Yours is a doomed commodity.
Maybe after a year or two
We shall get over missing you.
We shall forget how it used to be
To wake to your morning melody;
To hear through the drip of city rain
Some ghost that stirs in an old refrain.
We can get used to anything,
To concrete playgrounds and brownstone Spring!

Gypsies

Last night the gypsies came—
Nobody knows from where.
Where they've gone to nobody knows,
And nobody seems to care!

Between the trees on the old swamp road
I saw them round their fire:
Tattered children and dogs that barked
As the flames leaped high and higher;
There were black-eyed girls in scarlet shawls,
Old folk wrinkled with years,
Men with handkerchiefs round their throats
And silver loops in their ears.
Ragged and red like maple leaves
When frost comes in the fall,
The gypsies stayed but a single night;
In the morning gone were all—
Never a shaggy gypsy dog,
Never a gypsy child;
Only a burnt-out gypsy fire
Where danced that band so wild.

All gone and away,
Who knows where?
Only the wind that sweeps
Maple branches bare.

Prettymarsh

What is this place that it should bear
A name so salty-sweet and fair?
A name to tease my mind with brown
Tide flats about a scattered town
Of clapboard houses, squarely set
Behind their phlox and mignonette;
Their larkspur, lilies and sweet-peas;
Where wine-glass elms and apple trees
Shake out their shadows on the grass;
Where blue-wheeled carts and hayloads pass,
And ships with patched sails slowly ply
A crooked course when tides are high,
Or tilt their darkened hulls where grow
Keen-smelling weeds when tides are low;
Where Time seems but a shadow traced
Upon the church clock's numbered face.
Dear Prettymarsh, I shall not go
To see if you are really so.
What need, when letters on a sign
Can make you so completely mine?

A Rhyme for Greenwich Village

I walked on Eighth Street in the Spring,
   I thought I didn't care.
I bought French pastry by the L,
   Arbutus in the Square.
By Patchin Place I lingered
   Beneath the Tower clock,
I had forgotten how lost things
   Can throng a city block.
At Christopher and Gay Streets
   My knees began to shake,
And I gave an organ-man a dime
   For old times' sake.

Great-Uncle Willie

High on our dining-room wall,
Smiling and little and neat,
For years Great-Uncle Willie
Has watched us sit and eat.
Breakfast, dinner, supper,
Parties and afternoon tea—
I can't help thinking sometimes
How hungry he must be!
But he never looks reproachful,
Though cruel it must seem
To be a family portrait
On days when there's ice cream!

Roads

A road might lead to anywhere—
  To harbor towns and quays,
Or to a witch's pointed house
  Hidden by bristly trees.
It might lead past the tailor's door,
  Where he sews with needle and thread,
Or by Miss Pim the milliner's,
  With her hats for every head.
It might be a road to a great, dark cave
  With treasure and gold piled high,
Or a road with a mountain tied to its end,
  Blue-humped against the sky.
Oh, a road might lead you anywhere—
  To Mexico or Maine.
But then, it might just fool you, and—
  Lead you back home again!

Animals

Everywhere

Parade

This is the day the circus comes
With blare of brass, with beating drums,
And clashing cymbals, and with roar
Of wild beasts never heard before
Within town limits. Spick and span
Will shine each gilded cage and van;
Cockades at every horse's head
Will nod, and riders dressed in red
Or blue trot by. There will be floats
In shapes like dragons, thrones and boats,
And clowns on stilts; freaks big and small,
Till leisurely and last of all
Camels and elephants will pass
Beneath our elms, along our grass.

Mouse's Tail

A mouse's tail is a lovely thing,
It makes the nicest kind of swing.
But mice are selfish creatures, they
Always try to run away!

Early Morning

After the forty troubled days
  And nights of huddled dark;
After the perilous, shifting ways
  Of Noah's crowded Ark,
How frantic must the cloven feet
  Of deer and antelope
Have sped through fern and grasses sweet
  On Ararat's steep slope.
How must the leopard, goat, and hare;
  The chipmunk and the mouse
Have hailed that wood without a snare
  In rapturous carouse.
How must each drooping monkey tail
  With ecstasy have curled;
With what sedate delight the snail
  Have paced a rooted world.
How clear, across the barren waste,
  Flood-swept and watery,
Must every bird in liquid haste
  Have called from bush and tree.
Only the dove, bedraggled, weak,
  Too spent to coo or preen,
Must cling with damp and stubborn beak
  To her one leaf of green.

Something Told the Wild Geese

Something told the wild geese
   It was time to go.
Though the fields lay golden
   Something whispered,— "Snow."
Leaves were green and stirring,
   Berries, luster-glossed,
But beneath warm feathers
   Something cautioned,— "Frost."
All the sagging orchards
   Steamed with amber spice,
But each wild breast stiffened
   At remembered ice.
Something told the wild geese
   It was time to fly,—
Summer sun was on their wings,
   Winter in their cry.

Acrobat

Surely that is not a man
   Balanced on a thread in air,
But a brightly colored fan
   Folding and unfolding there?

Epilogue

Nothing now to mark the spot
But a littered vacant lot;
Sawdust in a heap, and there
Where the ring was, grass worn bare
In a circle, scuffed and brown,
And a paper hoop the clown
Made his little dog jump through,
And a pygmy pony-shoe.

The Performing Seal

Who is so proud
As not to feel
A secret awe
Before a seal
That keeps such sleek
And wet repose
While twirling candles
On his nose?

Equestrienne

See, they are clearing the sawdust course
For the girl in pink on the milk-white horse.
Her spangles twinkle; his pale flanks shine,
Every hair of his tail is fine
And bright as a comet's; his mane blows free
And she points a toe and bends a knee,
The while his hoofbeats fall like rain
Over and over and over again.
And nothing that moves on land or sea
Will seem so beautiful to me
As the girl in pink on the milk-white horse
Cantering over the sawdust course.

Merry-Go-Round

Purple horses with orange manes,
   Elephants pink and blue,
Tigers and lions that never were seen
   In circus parade or zoo!
Bring out your money and choose your steed,
   And prance to delightsome sound.
What fun if the world would turn some day
   Into a Merry-Go-Round.

The Animal Store

If I had a hundred dollars to spend,
   Or maybe a little more,
I'd hurry as fast as my legs would go
   Straight to the animal store.

I wouldn't say, "How much for this or that?"—
   "What kind of a dog is he?"
I'd buy as many as rolled an eye,
   Or wagged a tail at me!

I'd take the hound with the drooping ears
   That sits by himself alone;
Cockers and Cairns and wobbly pups
   For to be my very own.

I might buy a parrot all red and green,
   And the monkey I saw before,
If I had a hundred dollars to spend,
   Or maybe a little more.

Questions for a Flying Squirrel
to Answer

Who are you that can fly,
Or hide in a crumpled leaf;
To whom my hand is a vast
Pink plain of space and wonder?
Who breathed on your sleek, gray coat
That it should be thistledown soft,
And thicker than velvet mullein?
How were your whiskers spun,
More fine than silver thread?
Why are your claws so frail,
Like frost, with as eerie a coldness?
How came your tail to be
Flat as dove's breast-feather?
Who taught you to fold it close
In a curl about your haunches?
Why are your eyes so black,
So restless and ever shining
Under your pointed ears?
And how can a small heart beat
So fast in a tiny body?

Epitaph for a Scotch Terrier

Pause a moment by this spot
Whether you have dogs or not.
Here four blunt paws now quiet lie
That once went gayly padding by.
Here rests a tail that never grew
Too limp for making glad to-do.
Here mute, a bell from harness hung,
That often through green woods has rung,
And here a heart that put to shame
Others that pass for such in name.

Gunga

With wrinkled hide and great frayed ears,
Gunga the elephant, appears.
Colored like city smoke he goes
As gingerly on blunted toes
As if he held the earth in trust
And feared to hurt the very dust.

The Dancing Bear

Slowly he turns himself round and round,
  Lifting his paws with care,
Twisting his head in a sort of bow
  To the people watching there.
His keeper, grinding a wheezy tune,
  Jerks at the iron chain,
And the dusty, patient bear goes through
  His solemn tricks again.
Only his eyes are still and fixed
  In a wide, bewildered stare,
More like a child's lost in woods at night
  Than the eyes of a big brown bear.

Years Ago

Years Ago

Years ago and years ago
We gathered ground-pine in the snow,
In a wooded place beyond the glen.
I was eight years old and you were ten.
We wore red mittens and mufflers tied
Up to our noses. A blue-jay cried;
Tree-trunk shadows across the snow
Wavered as blue as indigo.
There were tracks of squirrel and deer and hare,
Delicate claw prints everywhere.
We spoke in whispers it was so still,
And we found a beautiful black crow quill.
Then twilight came and a thread of moon
On December's shortest afternoon.
Lights in the town shone, small and clear,
They were playing carols as we drew near
The old brick church. We called "Hello"
When someone laughed to see us go,
Each like a walking Christmas tree.
"I know a secret," you said to me
By your snowy gate where the hemlock grew,
And I whispered back, "I know one, too."

A Valentine for Old Dolls

Let others sing of cooing doves,
Of beating hearts and new-found loves,
These my poor rhymes shall tell the graces
Of china, wax, or wooden faces;
The charm of curls and painted braids,
Oh, sweet, perennially cheerful maids.
Your smiles shall last though nations fall,
And the young hands that dressed you all
In flowered flounces and ribbons gay,
Long since to dust be laid away.
Your years you wear like faint perfume
Of rose-leaves in a quiet room,
When winter at the threshold knocks;
Like some old tune a music-box
Tinkles as soft as phantom rain
Falling beyond a window pane.
And so, where'er you be today—
On parlor shelf; packed snug away
In attic camphor—still I'll praise
Your stiff-set limbs, your timeless gaze,
Knowing full well when I am gone
Thus you will sit, and thus smile on.

The Sampler

A strange, strange thing it is to know
My name was yours once long ago!
You answered to it as I do,
For then it just belonged to you.
You worked each letter neat and small
Into that sampler on my wall,
And as you sewed them patiently
Never once dreamed there would be me
To wear your name for mine some day
When sampler threads should turn to gray.

Old Houses

I think old houses are like Grandmothers,
With lilacs for their purple-ribbon bows,
Their upper windows square as spectacles;
And most of all a look—as if they watched
The road for someone, gone so long ago
That only they remember who it was
And why they wait there patiently all day.

Grandmother's Brook

Grandmother tells me about a brook
   She used to pass on her way to school;
A quick, brown brook with a rushing sound,
   And moss green edges, thick and cool.
When she was the age that I am now
   She would cross over it, stone by stone,
I like to think how she must have looked
   Under the greenery, all alone.

Sometimes I ask her:—"Is it there,
   That brook you played by,—the same, to-day?"
And she says she hasn't a doubt it is—
   It's children who change and go away.

For a Doll's House

My mind exactly fits this place
   For, being undersize,
This furniture in proper scale
   Its every want supplies;
The garlands on the rug so gay,
   A rosewood chair to please,
The sofa where a tired mind
   May rest in tufted ease;
A dressing table small enough
   To charm Titania's daughter
With looking glass as round and bright
   As a new-minted quarter;
A lamp in ivory and blue,
   And, since a mind must sup,
A china tea-set, buff and gold,
   With sprigs on every cup.

Queen Katherine of England

(AFTER SEEING "HENRY VIII")

Oh, had I lived in England then,
Most tender and most tragic Queen,
I would have walked the London streets
And waited there till I had seen
You pass, in all the pageantry
Of Henry's court. When he put by
Your love for lighter laughter, I
Would have sought out your fallen throne,
The castle where you grieved alone.
There I had brought you flowers sweet
From hillsides warm, and at your feet
I'd crouch, that I might look into
Your eyes, grown gray and dark with tears
Shed for an alien land and King
Through long and wearying years.
Oh, then, if you had noticed me—
A child amidst your company,
I would have begged your leave to stay
There by your side, that I might say,
In after years, these eyes had seen
A crownless, but unconquered Queen.

.80.

The Little Old Window

This window is very old, they say;
   Its little panes are queer.
You look through some, and things seem far
   That really are quite near.
This one has dimples in the glass,
   And the blurry pane I know
Is where a lady must have cried
   At the window long ago.

The Old Music Box

It's not the tunes that it can play,
But something else. I can never say
Whether it's more like falling rain
Far, far away, in France or Spain;
Or a hurrying brook, or the delicate din
When a humming bird begins to spin
Its rainbow wings; or the drone of bees,
Or something that is none of these.
But always under the tinkling part,
You can hear it beating like a heart,
Or the tick of tiny fairy clocks
Hidden away in the music box.

Family Pew

I wonder if my Great-Grandmother felt
   Air half so keen and sweet with salt and bay
On such a summer Sunday as she knelt
   In this old pew and heard the Parson pray?

I wonder if she saw white clouds stream by
   Through that same narrow window, if the trees
Were darkly green against so blue a sky,
   Pointing their tips as solemnly as these?

I wonder if she heard such gay birds sing
   Above the sermon and doxology;
If she was glad for each shrill twittering,
   For hum of bees and boom of distant sea?

Beneath some prim and flower-patterned dress
   Did her heart stir, as mine, to quickened beat?
And was she dumb in sudden thankfulness
   That she was young, and the round earth so sweet?

The Sea

A House I Know

Under the looming hills
Stands a house I know,
With its face turned to the sea.
About it fir trees grow,
And a little garden place
Where tangled color burns
And the air is bitter-sweet
With salt and flowers, by turns.
In that house I know,
Lamp and firelight blend
With the words that come and go
From friend to Island friend.

If Once You Have Slept on an Island

If once you have slept on an island
  You'll never be quite the same;
You may look as you looked the day before
  And go by the same old name,

You may bustle about in street and shop;
  You may sit at home and sew,
But you'll see blue water and wheeling gulls
  Wherever your feet may go.

You may chat with the neighbors of this and that
  And close to your fire keep,
But you'll hear ship whistle and lighthouse bell
  And tides beat through your sleep.

Oh, you won't know why, and you can't say how
  Such change upon you came,
But—once you have slept on an island
  You'll never be quite the same!

Tides

The tide is high! The tide is high!
The shiny waves go marching by
Past ledge and shallow and weedy reach
Up the long gray lengths of shingle beach;
Like an army storming height on height
With green-blue armor and banners white
On, on they charge to the farthest line
Of scattered seaweed brown and fine—
So far, then grumbling, back creep they,
And the tide has turned for another day.

The tide is low! The tide is low!
Weed-decked and gaunt the ledges show
With mussel shells in blues and blacks
And barnacles along their backs.
Now kelp shines like mahogany
And every rock pool brims with sea
To make a little looking glass
For sky and clouds and birds that pass.

Islands

All the islands have run away
  From the land which is their mother;
Out where the lighthouse guards the bay
  They race with one another.

Rocky or wooded, humped and small,
  Edged whitely round with spray,
What should we do if the islands all
  Ran back to land some day?

How would the ships know where to steer?
  Where would the sea-gulls fly?
How flat the sea would look, and queer,
  How lonely under the sky!

This Afternoon

Now hills retreat in amethyst;
Peaked Sargent wears a cap of mist.
The sun has found a far, white spire
And touched the tip to pagan fire.
In port the sea-turned windows twinkle
Like specks of mica. Lax sails wrinkle
As boats put in. Kelp ruddy shines
To mark the tide's last boundary lines.
In tattered ranks that storm the land
Dark on their point the spruces stand.
Gleaming as shells that shine through foam
Sunset is taking the sea-gulls home.

Grace for an Island Meal

Bless this board and bless this bread.
Bless this skylight over head
Through which any eye may see
Wheeling gull and blowing tree.
Bless this cloth of woven blue.
Bless these chanterelles* that grew
In secret under mossy bough.
Bless the Island pastured cow
For her milk which now we pour.
Bless these berries from the shore.
Bless every fresh laid egg and then
Blessings on each Island hen.
Bless the sweet smelling bowl of bay;
This tea from islands far away.
Bless spoon, and plate, and china cup,
The places set for us to sup
In sight of sky, in sound of sea—
Bless old and young, bless You and Me.

*A variety of mushroom.

Marooned

Narrow River is salty blue,
   The thorn trees shine and blur.
Along the humped backs of the dunes
   Sand grass grows thick as fur.
Gulls wheel and settle like falling snow,
   White flakes in the summer sun.
But darkly tilted, its mast awry,
   Is an old ship's skeleton,—
Marooned as never a ship should be,
Prow turned inland and stern to sea.

I'd Like To Be a Lighthouse

I'd like to be a lighthouse
   All scrubbed and painted white.
I'd like to be a lighthouse
   And stay awake all night
To keep my eye on everything
   That sails my patch of sea;
I'd like to be a lighthouse
   With the ships all watching me.

Familiarity

Those who live by the sea
Too familiar grow
With the changing ways of it,
And its magic ebb and flow.
Nothing they see or care to know
Save when will the tide be high or low.

Though green waves glitter
With white flung spray,
By their kitchen fires
They bend all day.
They turn their backs on the selfsame sea
That can make the heart leap up in me!

On Christmas

When Mary...

When Mary rode with Joseph
    And frost was in the air,
And all the roads were crowded,
    And no room anywhere—
Most welcome must the stable roof
    Have loomed that sheltered Her,
The scent of hay and straw more sweet
    Than Magi's gift of myrrh.

When Mary heard the singing
    Of far, angelic band,
She trembled at those solemn words
    She could not understand.
The tidings they were telling
    Were thorns upon Her breast—
It was the doves' familiar sound
    That set Her heart at rest.

When Mary left the stable
    With Joseph at Her side,
An Angel led the way before
    To guard Her Newborn Pride.
But Mary turned Her head away
    From heights of Paradise
To bless a manger filled with hay
    And humble, watching eyes.

Christmas Candle

Small hands I lift to You who once were small.
Small gifts I bring to You who, in a stall,
Brought to the world the greatest gift of all
   That winter night.

Small as a cricket's chirp the voice I raise
To join the chorus of enduring praise,
Yet once Your voice was small amid the maze
   Of singing might.

Small is the lighted taper that I bear,
But You will see it in the window there—
And for the sake of children everywhere
   Will bless its light.

For Christmas

Now not a window small or big
But wears a wreath or holly sprig;
Nor any shop too poor to show
Its spray of pine or mistletoe.
Now city airs are spicy-sweet
With Christmas trees along each street,
Green spruce and fir whose boughs will hold
Their tinseled balls and fruits of gold.
Now postmen pass in threes and fours
Like bent, blue-coated Santa Claus.
Now people hurry to and fro
With little girls and boys in tow,
And not a child but keeps some trace
Of Christmas secrets in his face.

Post-Christmas Rhyme

Before the festive berries fall
  Like jeweled rain; before the tree
That stands in aromatic green
  Is stripped of shining finery;
Before the heart's high brimming cup
  Holds one drop less of fiery dew—
Pray God that all of us may keep
  One Christmas spark the whole year through.

City Lights

Into the endless dark
The lights of the buildings shine,
Row upon twinkling row,
Line upon glistening line.
Up and up they mount
Till the tallest seems to be
The topmost taper set
On a towering Christmas tree.

Legend

Once every year the legend goes,
Before the first faint prick of rose
(Prophetic of a sharper thorn)
Stabs through the east on Christmas morn,
While sleepy folk lie snug abed,
In stable, barn, and narrow shed
No bird or beast that must not stir
From feathered dreams, from drowsy fur,
For in that moment each of them
Is linked to far-off Bethlehem
By some rough-coated ancestor
Who whinnied at the stable door
When Wise Men knocked; by some shy beast
Who hailed strange brightness in the east
With anxious bark, and startled bleat,
With muffled coo, and padding feet;
With soft cries immemorial
Echoed from eave-swung nest and stall.
While from the frosty dark immense,
Doomed to a golden permanence,
The weather-cock may shed his curse
Of traitor's warning, to rehearse
More shrill than carols of the blest
His ancient:—"Christus natus est!"

City Christmas

I will go walking in our town
   Now that it's Christmas time
To see the streets of shops all decked
   Gay as a pantomime.
There will be patchwork and cuckoo-clocks;
   Angels of marzipan;
Green glass bottles and picture books
   In their jackets spick and span.
There will be trinkets and toys galore,
   Candles for every tree
Stacked at the curb in spicy green
   Bristling and needle-y.
There will be children with dimes to spend;
   Stars in the queerest places;
Lights that twinkle and lights that glow,
   And lights in people's faces.
I will go walking in our town,
   Knowing that all is well—
Seeing the sights of Christmas,
   Smelling each Christmas smell.

Christmas Goes to Sea

I saw a fishing boat steer by,
Blunt-prowed beneath the winter sky,
  As Christmas dusk was falling.

The hull was crusted dark with spray,
The waters all about spread gray,
  And sea gulls followed calling.

But to the masthead gallantly
Was lashed a little Christmas tree,
  A green-armed pledge of pine.

No bright festoons or gifts it bore,
And yet those empty boughs held more
  Than tinsel for a sign.

So fair a sight it was to see—
That small, seafaring Christmas tree
  High amid shroud and spar.

And all night long I thought of it
Salt-drenched, wind-buffeted, and lit
  By Bethlehem's bright star.

Christmas Trees

Each year they stand by curb and store
Green-armed and fragrant, score on score—
A dark and immemorial frieze
Of waiting, new-cut Christmas trees.

More fair those sturdy boughs to see
Than wealth of tinseled finery.
More sweet that spice of spruce and fir
Than fabled frankincense and myrrh.

Yet every waiting Christmas tree
Keeps faith with human destiny,
Standing, as they have always stood,
Nailed fast to crosses made of wood.

Fairy Folk

Elves, Go Fetch Your Lanterns

Elves, go fetch your lanterns:
Light up every pine cone
Where the woods are thickest,
Lest, when darkness falls
Black as any witch-cloak,
Baby birds should wake and cry
Fearful in the dark.

Elfin Buttons

If ever I should find
An Elf button bright,
I'd sew it on my coat
With strong thread and tight.
I wouldn't take it off—
Not even at night,
For there'd be no telling
When that wee Elf might
Come for to whisk it
Out of my sight.
But if he did
I'd tell him true—
"Wherever that button goes
I GO TOO!"

Young Elf Ladies

When moonlight spangles the tops of trees,
　Elves do exactly as they please,
They sing, they skip, they dance a reel,
　According as to how they feel.

Up all the Young Elf Ladies go,
　Fleetly dancing on tip-toe,
Gossamer skirts and blowing hair,
　Tripping it up and down the air,

　　Till even the fleetest Lady Elf
　　Never can catch up with herself.

Elfin Handkerchiefs

No one knows the reason why
Elves can't catch cold and they never cry.
But any sunny day you may spy
On fields and lawns all under the sky
Their cobweb handkerchiefs spread to dry!

The Seven Ages of Elf-hood

When an Elf is as old as a year and a minute
He can wear a cap with a feather in it.

By the time that he is two times two
He has a buckle for either shoe.

At twenty he is fine as a fiddle,
With a little brown belt to go round his middle.

When he's lived for fifty years or so
His coat may have buttons all in a row.

If past three score and ten he's grown
Two pockets he has for his very own.

At eighty-two or three years old
They bulge and jingle with bits of gold.

But when he's a hundred and a day
He gets a little pipe to play!

Half Past Eight

Creaking stairs and bed for me—
For lucky ones somewhere
A curtain of light goes sliding up,
And Peter Pan is there.

Somewhere the other children see
Hook and his pirate band
Seeking the Lost Boys snugly hid
In the Never, Never Land.
Others will save poor Tinker Bell,
And I not there to help;
When Peter pipes from his tree-top house
He'll not pipe to myself!

If wishes did all they ought to do
Things would not be this way—
Those other children would go to bed,
And I would be at the play.

The Pointed People

I don't know who they are,
But when it's shadow time
In woods where the trees crowd close,
With bristly branches crossed,
From their secret hiding places
I have seen the Pointed People
Gliding through brush and bracken.
Maybe a peakèd cap
Pricking out through the leaves,
Or a tiny pointed ear
Up-cocked, all brown and furry,
From ferns and berry brambles,
Or a pointed hoof's sharp print
Deep in the tufted moss,
And once a pointed face
That peered between the cedars,
Blinking bright eyes at me
And shaking with silent laughter.

Elfin Berries

"Elf, will you sell me your berries bright
  For to make me a pot of jam?"

"No, for they grew in Fairyland,
  I'm very sorry, ma'am."

"Not if I let you lick the spoon
  When the sweet juice bubbles red?"

"My berries are not for pots and spoons
  Or earthen crocks," he said,
"They came from a bush that no man knows
  Whose name is 'Never-Grow-Old,'
And they shall be meat and drink to me,
  And warmth when the nights are cold."

"Here's a ring, Sweet Elf, and a purse of gold,
And beads as blue as the sea—?"

"Elfin berries are not for sale,
  Good-day to you, ma'am!" said he.

The Butterfly Trainers

Butterflies didn't always know
How to spread their wings and go
Gliding down the slopes of air
On their spangled wings and fair;
Never dared to leave the land
Till the elves took them in hand,
Made them bridle, bit and reins
Out of shiny corn silk skeins;
Drove them through the long blue hours,
Introducing them to Flowers.

Almost

There are things you almost see
    In the woods of evening—
Fairies as thick as fireflies,
    Elves leaping in a ring.

There are things you almost hear
    When no one passes by—
Stirring of seeds in good damp earth,
    Stars marching through the sky.

Green Riders

When there's hardly a breath of wind to stir
The pasture grass and juniper,
Yet they rise and fall like green sea tides
Showing their hidden silver sides,
Then you may know the Elves are near,
You may hear their horns blow faint and clear,
Or see an Elfin Rider pass
Straddling each green and bending grass.

Pygmy Song

If I were no taller than father's thumb
My loaf would be this wheaten crumb.
I'd wash in a thimbleful of dew,
With a green grass blade I'd tie my shoe;
Feast on a strawberry, wild and red,
And hang my wash on a spider's thread.
I'd steer my course on a rockpool sea,
And a butterfly my plane would be.
But if by chance I lost my way
In forests of fern where green fronds sway,
In mossy hollow, on perilous foam—
Firefly lanterns would light me home.

Elfin Town

I saw the roofs of Elfin Town
   All peaked and pointed gay,
And scores of Elfin chimney-pots
   Smoke-wreathed in blue or gray;
While higher than the Elfin eaves
   Grew shady clover trees,
Some red, some white, but all a-stir
   With humming, gold-winged bees.
I saw the lawns all bright with dew,
   The Elfin windows shine,
And frocks of greenest gossamer
   Hung on a cobweb line.
I heard the tread of Elfin feet;
   A spinning-wheel's soft whirring,
And kettles on an Elfin fire
   Make low and pleasant purring.
From grassy pastures round about
   The bells of Elfin sheep
Went tinkle-tankle drowsily
   From steep to sunny steep.
And sweetly Elfin fiddles scraped,
   And clearly shrilled the horn:—
"Child, Child, come back to Elfin Town
   For it's here that you were born!"

Index of First Lines

811
F

20,846

Field, Rachel Lyman

Poems